Demos is an independent think tank committed to radical thinking on the long-term problems facing the UK and other advanced industrial societies.

It aims to develop ideas – both theoretical and practical – to help shape the politics of the twenty-first century, and to improve the breadth and depth of political debate.

Demos publishes books and a regular journal and undertakes substantial empirical and policy oriented research projects. Demos is a registered charity.

In all of its work Demos brings together people from a wide range of backgrounds in business, academia, government, the voluntary sector and the media to share and cross-fertilise ideas and experiences.

For further information and
subscription details please contact:
Demos
Panton House
25 Haymarket
London
SW1Y 4EN

email: mail@demos.co.uk
www.demos.co.uk

Patient Power

Choice for a better NHS

Peter Lilley

First published in
June 2000

by Demos
Panton House
25 Haymarket
London
SW1Y 4EN

Arguments 24
ISBN 1 84180 035 X

Contents

Acknowledgements

I am grateful to Cynthia Wu, Maud Pelletier and Chris Muller for their invaluable help with resaerch; to a large number of people working in the NHS who have commented on drafts in confidence; and above all to Christine Percival for nurturing it through innumerable drafts.

Executive summary

1. Growing discontent with the NHS is not simply the result of a shortfall in resources and will not be cured only by spending more. It reflects increasingly consumerist attitudes. Patients expect to exercise choice, to be given options, to receive information and advice and to criticise inadequacies.

2. The old NHS is ill-suited to cope with this new desire for choice and diversity. It is monolithic, centralised, secretive and producer dominated.

3. The government has pursued the command and control approach, further centralising decisions and seeking greater uniformity of provision. This reduces diversity, delegation and responsiveness to patients' preferences.

(iv) Recent reforms have effectively eliminated the last vestiges of patient and GP choice. Since April 1999, patients and their GPs can no longer choose to go to a hospital with a shorter waiting time, or a better success rate, or which is nearer relatives than that selected by their local health bureaucracy.

(v) The new system is causing a crisis in specialist provision and forcing patients to have specialised treatment in general hospitals.

Value of choice

1. Choice works in every other service to drive up quality, cut costs and respond to users' preferences. It should be harnessed to do the same within the health service.

2. Where users can choose between alternatives, suppliers must match the quality and cost of the best. Otherwise they lose users and revenues.

3. The key to making choice effective within a public service like the NHS is to make the taxpayers' money follow the patient's choice to fund the hospital they select.

History of choice

1. Before the NHS was set up patients had the right to choose their hospital and their money went directly to it.

2. When the NHS was set up patients retained the right to be referred by their GP to the hospital of their choice. But taxpayers' money no longer went automatically to that hospital. When tight budgeting was introduced, the most popular hospitals overspent and had to close wards.

3. The 1991 reforms began to curtail GPs' freedom to refer patients to their chosen hospitals. However, GPs could still make extra-contractual referrals.

4. The 1999 reforms effectively ended GPs' right to refer patients to the hospital of their choice by abolishing extra-contractual referrals. So although the right of referral has not been legally abolished, it has been effectively ended by administrative regulations.

Criticisms

1. Ministers have opposed proposals to restore patient choice on a number of (conflicting) grounds. That:

   - 'such choice never existed'. Yet it has since the NHS was founded.
   - 'it has not been legally abolished'. Instead it has been administratively strangled.
   - 'all hospitals should be made equally good'. This is a counsel of perfection or recipe for mediocrity. Anyway, patients may

wish to choose between clinically equal hospitals on non-clinical grounds.

- 'it was necessary to end internal market bureaucracy'. As Lord Winston blurted out, the internal market and the purchaser/provider split still exist.
- 'they had to stop 'hospital competing against hospital''. That is old Labour prejudice. Choice would make hospitals strive for patients, not against each other.
- 'extra-contractual referrals led to disputes over who pays'. This is a serious point, though similar problems exist with out-of-area treatments. Making individual referral the norm with money following the patient should remove conflict.
- 'patients choice is a prelude to privatising the NHS'. This is nonsense – my aim is to give choice *within* the NHS to the vast majority who can't afford private healthcare.

Information

1. To make informed choices patients and GPs need information on waiting times, specialisation and clinical outcomes of each hospital. Much of this data exists but is not published. It should be available in GPs' surgeries and on the internet.

2. Mortality rates are the most controversial and need adjustment for pre-operative condition plus interpretation.

3. US experience shows how a combination of information, publication and choice can be a powerful weapon in improving clinical outcomes.
4. GPs would need to become patients' advocates and advisers not agents of the health bureaucracy. This new attitude among GPs may be stimulated by a growing trend of patients towards self-diagnosis and referral via NHS Direct and Online.

Specialisation

1. Abolition of extra-contractual referrals is causing a crisis in specialist centres, as highlighted by the president of the Royal College of Surgeons.

2. Even prior to this, limits on choice meant best practice developed in one specialist centre did not spread to others.

3. There is little scope for hospitals to specialise in *common* treatments. Given freedom of referral specialist centres would develop more easily – generating the improvements in quality and efficiency that normally flow from specialisation.

Quality

1. Choice drives up quality – not only of clinical outcomes. Choice would draw attention to the problems of cleanliness, re-infection and shoddy nursing which are tolerated in some NHS hospitals at present.

2. Hospitals would also be encouraged to develop diverse styles of care and cater for subjective preferences – single sex wards, consultants of same sex, information about alternative treatments and so on.

Efficiency

1. Under the old 'internal markets', each hospital set charges equal to their costs. The system was open to criticism that it encouraged purchasers to send patients to the cheapest hospital.

2. The new system of setting a standard charge for each category of treatment avoids that criticism. The purchaser clearly has no incentive to sacrifice quality for cost.

3. The new system still gives hospitals an incentive to reduce costs to the standard level.

Feasibility

1. There is bound to be resistance to more choice from those used to the NHS command and control model, who cannot conceive how a system involving multiple decision-makers interacting with each other can work.

2. In fact, the law of large numbers means a fairly stable pattern of referrals will emerge; patient movements are likely to be gradual and at the margin.

3. That will give less popular hospitals both an incentive and time to improve patient care. They must be free to change personnel to re-build confidence.

(4. Where closure or merger of an inadequate hospital or department is the only solution, it provokes a political storm under the present system. If such changes were brought about by patients voting with their feet, it would help defuse the political rows that currently impede change.

Proposals

1. The majority who depend entirely on the NHS need more opportunity to exercise informed choice *within* the NHS.

2. This requires three key steps:

   a. Restore the right of GPs to refer patients to the hospital of their choice
   b. Publish information by speciality and by hospital on waiting times, frequency of performing treatments, mortality rates (adjusted for severity of condition), avoidable re-admissions and so on. Make that information available in GPs' surgeries and on the internet.
   c. Make taxpayers' money follow patients choice simply and speedily.

1. Introduction

The death of reverence is usually speedy but rarely painless. Until recently, the NHS was almost the only institution in Britain accorded universal reverence. Yet that respect is rapidly slipping away. It could not last in the face of consumerist attitudes, the questioning of established authority and a growing desire to take personal control over one's own healthcare.

During the 1980s, it was possible to quell criticism of the then government's record on the NHS by questioning the critics about their own experience of the NHS. Virtually everyone who had direct experience for themselves or their family would express complete satisfaction with the treatment they had received (although they invariably quoted worries they had heard from the staff or from the media about alleged threats to the NHS).

That is no longer the normal response. Almost overnight, patients became much more critical of their experiences in the hands of the NHS.

It would be wrong to pretend that this new dissatisfaction is all the fault of this Labour government. The increase in waiting times to see consultants about serious conditions as a result of the politically motivated focus on waiting lists may have aggravated the problem. But the more critical attitude taken by patients and their relatives undoubtedly began to emerge under the last Conservative government. It was actively fostered by the Patients' Charter. The cause is probably more a spontaneous change in people's attitudes rather than a deterioration in the service they receive.

The new attitudes also affect patient behaviour. NHS managers say that the sharp rise in the use of accident and emergency services during the winter months in recent years is at least partly due to new attitudes. A growing number of people take an 'off-the-shelf' attitude to healthcare. For example, people are no longer prepared to wait to discover whether a sore throat will develop into a lost voice. Still less are they willing to take time off work to queue up in a doctor's surgery. Instead they go to hospital accident and emergency units on the way to work asking for something to suppress the symptoms.

People are becoming more 'consumerist'. They like to exercise choices. They want the information and advice to do so sensibly. They expect a diverse range of options. And they are critical of inadequacies.

This is affecting all public services. As a result, the central issue within the public sector in future will be managing choice and diversity.

It is, however, hard to imagine any institution less well designed to cater for these new attitudes than the NHS. It is monolithic, centralised, secretive and producer dominated. Worse still, it aims to provide an increasingly uniform service across the country that will inevitably further limit the scope for diversity, delegation and responsiveness.

Discussion about the NHS revolves almost exclusively around the need for more money. The Left sees that coming from higher taxes – possibly made more palatable by the hypothecation of a health tax. Some on the Right hope that promoting the private sector will relieve some of the demand on the NHS or that compulsory insurance will prove less unpopular than straightforward taxation.

The extraordinary feature of the March 2000 budget was setting targets for spending more money on health. To set targets for improving healthcare or health outcomes would make some sense. But spending more money as an end in itself is bizarre. Trying to match the health outcomes of other countries (if they are better than our own which is far from certain)[1] would be a rational objective that may require higher spending. Trying to spend as much as they do is wholly irrational.

Doubtless more money is needed.[2] However, new money will not be enough. We also need to ensure that it is used more efficiently and in ways which satisfy patients' desires rather than bureaucratic needs.

NHS patients want to choose, they should be allowed more choice, but instead they are being deprived of what little choice they have.

Tony Blair recognised this desire for choice in his party conference speech last year. Parodying his predecessor, Margaret Thatcher, he said 'I want to go to the hospital of my choice, on the day I want, at the time I want. And I want it on the NHS.' In practice, however, the government contradicts itself. The reforms it introduced in April 1999 effectively abolish the last vestiges of patient choice in the NHS.

Under those reforms, patients and their GPs can no longer choose to go to a hospital with a shorter waiting time. Nor can they choose to go to a hospital with a better success rate in performing the treatment they need. They cannot even choose to save the NHS money by going to a hospital that is more efficient. They must go to the hospital selected by their local health bureaucracy.

The President of the Royal College of Surgeons highlighted the growing crisis this is causing:

> 'It is terribly important that a GP can refer a patient to the appropriate specialist centre. A new system under which extra-contractual referrals were abolished a year ago makes that more difficult. That is very disappointing and not right for the highest standards of patient care.'[3]

Loss of choice is causing a particularly severe crisis in some specialist centres and forcing patients to receive complex treatments in general hospitals. The resultant problems are one reason for the surge of discontent within the NHS that has caught the government by surprise

This essay is not intended to be a partisan polemic. So it must be acknowledged that the previous government's reforms also had the unintended consequence of restricting the ability of patients to select a hospital of their choice. My objective is not to prove that one government is worse than another. It is to explore the case for expanding patient choice within the NHS.

Choice has been abolished by stealth – by technical changes introduced in complex circulars. But the loss of choice has all too vivid consequences for sick people. When first I highlighted the need to restore choice I received a moving letter from a brave young woman, Helen Smith, explaining from her experience 'why choice is absolutely necessary'. As a result of meningococcal septicaemia she needed four artificial limbs. Her local hospital could only provide limbs that caused terrible blistering, damage and infection. She found another orthopaedic unit in Dorset that could tailor artificial limbs to her needs. But her health authority in East Anglia would not, or could not, transfer the funds to Dorset even though she was prepared to pay any extra if they were more expensive. Eventually she had to go there privately, paying the whole cost with the help of public donations. No thanks to the taxpayer she is now able to come off benefit and resume studying for her PhD. She concludes that 'the only way to improve the service is to allow patients to choose where they want to be treated. Then bad centres will shut down (or improve) and centres of excellence will develop'. Choice is about helping people like Helen.

I do not pretend that choice is a panacea. There is no single policy that will cure all the NHS's ailments. A wide range of measures, over and above increasing resources, will be needed to get the best out of the NHS. But increased patient choice can play a significant part in reinforcing these measures.

2. Value of choice

People want choice. It should not be the privilege of the better off. Yet that is the case at present. Only those who can afford to pay twice for health – once through their taxes and a second time through private medicine – get any real choice. Only some 15 per cent of households have any private health insurance. And most of them still rely on the NHS for a significant proportion of their care – accident and emergency, catastrophic and major surgery, and general practitioner services. Moreover, most only have insurance in their healthier years and fall back on the NHS in old age when they have greatest need of medical care.

Even if the proportion of people with private medical insurance could, by generous tax reliefs, be doubled (and I know of no one who thinks that is achievable in the foreseeable future) that would still leave 70 per cent of the population wholly dependent on the NHS.

They, too, want and would benefit from more choice *within* the NHS. This pamphlet is solely about extending choice to the overwhelming majority of our fellow citizens who depend on the NHS.

Most people are no longer content – if they ever were – to be treated like children, given only pocket money to spend on inessentials, while the big decisions are taken above their heads by the grown-ups, the bureaucrats. The demand for more choice and influence in areas like healthcare does not derive from ideology; it reflects profound social and educational change. People are increasingly accustomed to taking decisions over their own lives, at work and at home. And where choice is on the menu the appetite grows with eating.

We know that choice works in sectors where users do have choice. It is what drives the improvement in quality and efficiency in services. Suppliers of goods or services who do not match the quality or cost of the best alternative producers lose users and therefore revenues. So they have to do better.

Choice is effective in ordinary services because the user pays: the suppliers are rewarded by every user they attract, and thereby receive the resources to enable them to satisfy more users in future. There is no question of NHS patients being expected to pay individually for hospital care. But we can make patients' choices effective by ensuring that taxpayers' money follows them.

Conservative reforms have already shown that choice can bring similar benefits in public services. For example, what made parental choice in education really effective was 'making the money follow the pupil'. Before this, when parents chose to send their child to a particular school it did not receive any extra resources. As a result, the most popular schools ended up with the largest classes and the most overworked teachers. Conversely, the less popular schools that lost pupils did not suffer a corresponding reduction in resources. So they had smaller class sizes and less pressure on their teachers. Neither good schools nor poor schools had much incentive to do better.

Publishing exam results and school prospectuses enabled parents to make more informed choices. But it was 'formula funding' coupled with 'local management of schools' that made money follow the pupil and so gave parental choice real clout. As a result, popular schools that attracted more pupils were rewarded with extra resources. Less popular schools that lost pupils also lost resources. They were forced to pull up their socks and improve their standards.

The effect was often dramatic. Governing bodies that had previously tolerated inadequate head teachers now replaced them. Schools that had treated parental concern about exam results with disdain suddenly became interested in academic success. The net result has been improvement not just in good schools, but also in those that were initially less good. Making the money follow the pupil has also allowed schools to specialise (for instance, in technology, languages or music) where there is parental and pupil demand for that type of school.[4]

Now is the time to find ways to give NHS patients similar power by helping them and their GPs make informed choices that will determine where the money goes.

3. History of choice

It has been a long-standing tradition in Britain that consultants do not accept patients directly but only on referral from their general practitioner.[5] General practitioners in turn have had the right to refer patients to consultants according to their judgement of what is best for their patient.[6] This right does not seem to have been explicitly incorporated in the 1946 NHS Act. It probably did not seem necessary to reaffirm it precisely because it was taken for granted.

Subsequently, however, governments have restated that right – most recently in the Patients Charter 1991. This affirms that 'to be referred to a consultant, acceptable to you when your GP thinks it necessary' is 'every citizen['s] established National Health Service right'. It is also enshrined in secondary legislation: NHS (General Medical Services) Regulations 1992 state 'general practitioners may arrange for the referral of patients, as appropriate, for the provision of services'.

Since patients had the right to be referred by their GP to the hospital of their choice before the NHS was established, the initial distribution of hospitals when the NHS was set up tended to reflect patient choice. The NHS simply allocated funds according to the needs of the existing hospitals in line with their previous budgets.

Over time, however, the population shifted. Some hospitals changed the facilities they offered. The spread of car ownership also meant that people could access different hospitals. So the distribution of resources became out of kilter with people's wants and needs. As the official history of the NHS admits, 'the continuing allocation of funds on the basis of the cost of maintaining existing services ... caused ossification of the existing pattern of expenditure'.[7]

The government therefore set up the Resource Allocation Working Party which reported in September 1976. It concluded that funds in each region ought to be allocated according to the needs of the population (as reflected in population, age and morbidity figures) and not the historic location of NHS buildings. Even though the shift of funding was carried out gradually, it caused a political trauma. Hospitals concentrated in old city centres, where populations were decreasing, lost resources and protested vigorously. Meanwhile MPs in areas of growing populations, which were relatively under-provided with hospitals, complained that the promised extra resources were not being delivered fast enough. The re-allocation of resources by political decree proved extremely uncomfortable.

Throughout this time, patients referred by their GPs were, in principle, free to go to the hospital of their choice. But their choice had little direct impact on how resources were allocated.

The patients could choose to go to a particular NHS hospital but the resources they provided as taxpayers were all too often dispatched elsewhere. So if a hospital was particularly good at treating patients and therefore attracted additional referrals, it would soon overspend its budget. Consequently, it was the most popular hospitals that had to close wards, cut back on their activity or refuse referrals from other districts. Less popular hospitals often escaped unscathed.

During the 1980s, the general public and, indeed, most MPs – who knew little about how resources were allocated within the NHS – were increasingly bewildered and angered by this apparently perverse sense of priorities.

It seemed as if 'they' – the managers who ran the NHS – had got it in for the most popular local hospitals. Either that, or overall NHS resources must be so inadequate that even the most popular hospitals and units had to close. The system certainly gave fuel to those who alleged that the Conservative government was underfunding and undermining the NHS.

The 1990 reforms: 'working for patients'

Growing concern (not least among Conservative MPs) about the state of the NHS led to the reforms that were developed in the late 1980s[8] and implemented in 1990.

The principal feature of these reforms was the separation of the function of purchasing healthcare from that of providing it – the so-called 'purchaser/provider split'. Local health authorities and larger GP practices that opted to become fundholders would purchase healthcare for people in their area or on their list. They would do so with a budget financed by the taxpayer and related to the number, age and morbidity of the local population. Healthcare would be provided by self-governing trusts running hospitals.

The idea was that money would follow the patient. In theory, therefore, this should have removed the paradox of the previous system, in which more successful hospitals were penalised, and sometimes closed, because they attracted additional patients but no additional resources. Many hoped that the purchaser/provider split would work like the system of money following pupils in the school system. That had been introduced recently and was already rewarding successful schools and giving less successful schools a strong incentive to improve.

However, in practice the new system required fundholders to negotiate contracts with each hospital. The fundholders would estimate how many of their patients would require each main type of surgery. They would then negotiate contracts to provide those treatments with appropriate general and specialist hospitals. Patients were then expected to go to the hospital with which their fundholder had contracted to provide the sort of care they required.

The introduction of the purchaser/provider split produced genuine benefits. In particular, it gave GP fundholders real clout when negotiating with hospitals. But it did not increase individual patient choice. Nonetheless, it remained possible for patients to be referred by their GP to hospitals other than those with which fundholders had contracted. The GP could make what was called an 'extra-contractual referral', or ECR.

ECRs made by health authorities accounted for only 2 per cent (£0.5 billion) of hospital expenditure, albeit an increase from the 1.3 per cent in 1991 when the reforms began (see Figure 1). These figures understate the true figure since they *exclude* extra-contractual referrals made by fundholding GPs, who account for about 17 per cent of health service spending in recent years.

Figure 1. Expenditure on ECRs by health authorities, 1991-92 to 1998-99

	ECR expenditure[1] £m	*HCHS expenditure[2] £m*	*ECR expenditure as % of HCHS*
1991/92	239	17,806	1.3%
1992/93	295	19,579	1.5%
1993/94	350	20,347	1.7%
1994/95	386	21,324	1.8%
1995/96	442	22,439	2.0%
1996/97	494	23,412	2.1%
1997/98	530	24,726	2.1%
1998/99	531	26,175	2.0%

1. ECR figures from unaudited HA in-year financial monitoring returns
2. HCHS figures from 1998 Departmental Report (Figure 2.1)

Moreover, the majority of these extra-contractual referrals were for emergency or tertiary services. It is estimated that less than 40 per cent were for elective treatments. And most elective ECRs were for small sums of money. The majority cost less than £500 with very few costing over £5,000. The cost of administering the system was about £22 million – 4 per cent of the total. (This cost ratio is similar for the NHS as a whole.) But referrals could be the subject of time-consuming debate about which budget should pay for them.[9]

Historically, patient movements across district and regional boundaries have been far greater than suggested by the figures for ECRs. However, Figure 2 (over) shows a decline in such movements since the health reforms introduced in 1991-92. Figures for earlier years were not collected centrally. Nor are any figures yet available showing the impact of the abolition of ECRs in 1999.

The 1999 reforms

It is disappointing that so few patients were in the past able to exercise choice over where they were treated. What is astonishing is that the government should find even that tiny degree of individual choice too much.

Yet they have abolished extra-contractual referrals entirely. And

Figure 2. Percentage of treatments carried out in NHS hospitals in health areas other than that in which the patient was resident, England 1990-91 to 1998-99[10] (including overseas residents)

	1990/91	1991/92	1992/93	1993/94	1994/95	1995/96	1996/97	1997/98	1998/99
Health authority	25.4	24.7	23.3	22.1	21.5	21.6	22.7	24.7	22.6
NHS region	9.0	7.9	7.4	7.7	7.1	7.4	6.5	8.9	6.8

the new system of primary care groups (PCGs), apart from being a wholly unnecessary upheaval introduced for ideological reasons, further restricts the scope for patient choice. The PCGs have to negotiate contracts (renamed service level agreements) on the basis of the forecast needs of all the patients in their area for at least three years ahead. Instead of the money following the patient, the patient will have to follow the money. Instead of strengthening patient choice the system imposes bureaucratic choice.

4. Criticisms of choice

My parliamentary questions about patient choice have evoked a surprisingly hostile and self-contradictory response from the government. On the first occasion, I was peremptorily told that patients had never had such a right to choose and on the next that their right to choose remained intact under the latest system. On other occasions, patient choice has been condemned because it is allegedly bureaucratic and costly; it causes hospitals to compete against each other; it would lead to specialisation in a few distant centres. I have also been told that it would be better to make all hospitals equally good; and that patients and even GPs are too ill-informed to exercise choice.

Some of these points are partisan, but others raise genuine issues that need to be addressed. It is worth considering these criticisms in turn.

'Patient choice has never existed in the NHS'

This was the claim of the junior Health Minister, John Denham.[11] By implication, patient choice is an irrelevant chimera alien to the way the NHS has always worked. In fact, as spelt out in chapter 3, patients with the consent of their GPs, have had the right to be referred to the consultant of their choice since the NHS began. Presumably, Denham was relying on the weasel word 'individual' in his assertion that 'no such choice ever existed for individual patients'.

No one is proposing that patients should exercise choice individually rather than in conjunction with their GP. Patients do nonetheless have the right to move to a different GP should they find it difficult to reach agreement on choice of consultant.

'Patient choice remains despite the abolition of extra-contractural referrals'

John Denham subsequently reversed his defence of the government's 1999 reforms and claimed that patients, in conjunction with their GPs, still have the right to be referred to any consultant: 'Nothing we have done removes clinicians' right to make the appropriate referral for a patient'.[12] He added that legislative change would be needed to remove it – a rather ominous indication that ministers may have thought about doing so. As explained in chapter 3, it is not at all clear whether, and if so where, this long-standing right is enshrined in primary legislation. But it is clear that even if the right has not been legally abolished, it has been administratively withdrawn. The abolition of ECRs is intended to have the effect of preventing GPs making referrals to consultants and trusts other than those selected by their PCGs. The Health Service circular 'Guidance on Out of Area Treatments [OATs]' states that 'the aim is ... to ensure that by 2000/01 OATs cover only an essential minimum of treatments. The OAT arrangements are intended to be used primarily for emergencies, typically where an individual is admitted to hospital for treatment while they are away from home'.[13] Nowhere in that key circular, which legally defines the new system, is there any reference to GPs or patients having any right of referral to a hospital other than those under service agreements with the local primary care group.

If a GP were to exercise his theoretical right to refer a patient to a hospital outside his primary care group agreement, the chosen hospital would in general simply refuse to accept the referral because they could not be sure they would be paid.

As the Director of the College of Health wrote about the replacement of extra-contractual referrals with out-of-area treatments: 'patients ... have less choice than ever in the NHS history'.[14]

'It is better to remove the inequalities which make choice attractive'

According to the health minister: 'It is much better to plan for the vast majority of patients to receive high quality services in their most local hospital, rather than ... patients have to chase all over the place to try to find out where the best treatment is available'.[15]

This is both a counsel of perfection and a recipe for mediocrity. It would be marvellous if every local hospital could simultaneously be raised to whatever is currently the highest available standard. But no one seriously believes that is possible. Equality is an ideal of the left-wing mind not a characteristic of the real world.

In practice, the only way it can be approximated with top-down planning is by stopping some hospitals drawing ahead of the pack in the quality of their medical care. It will always be easiest to redistribute resources away from hospitals that begin to emerge as centres of excellence, that develop better forms of treatment or that are simply run more efficiently. By contrast raising the standards of the average or below-average hospital by central direction is difficult, costly and time-consuming.

The NHS has never achieved equality of excellence in all its hospitals and the government has not indicated how it will achieve this previously unattainable goal in future. Indeed, the NHS has not been particularly good at identifying the less good hospitals, let alone reforming them.

The great advantage of allowing more patient choice is that it harnesses the desire of GPs and their patients continually to identify the hospitals that are best for their needs. And if money follows patient choice, it motivates the less good hospitals to emulate the better ones. The government hopes that eliminating differences between hospitals will remove the need for choice. The reality is that effective choice will constantly erode differences between hospitals by forcing the less good to improve.

Even if all hospitals were clinically identical, some patients would still wish to exercise choice. Some would want to go to out-of-area hospitals to be nearer relatives or friends who would then be able to visit them or care for them when they leave. Others who have moved house may want to go back to the hospital near their previous home that had treated them before. Continuity of care is a very legitimate concern.

Also, different hospitals emphasise different but equally valid clinical approaches. For example, the proportion of births delivered by Caesarean section ranges from 9 per cent to 25 per cent at different hospitals.[16] Likewise, some hospitals are more likely to perform hysterectomies than others. Women may prefer to be treated in hospitals where the approach accords with their own predisposition.

So even in the almost inconceivable event that it were possible to eliminate differences in clinical quality between hospitals, there would still be strong reasons for allowing patient choice.

Patient choice allegedly requires an 'incredibly costly bureaucratic system'[17]

The Labour Manifesto promised that 'Labour will abolish the Conservative 'internal market' in healthcare', 'releasing £100 million per annum of costs for use in frontline care'.

In his *New Statesman* interview, Lord Winston blurted out the truth before he was silenced – namely that the government 'has failed to eradicate the so-called internal market ... We still have an internal market, but instead of commissioning by local health authorities, we have primary care groups. I think we have been quite deceitful about it'.[18] They have indeed retained the key feature of the internal market – the purchaser/provider split – and merely renamed and altered its other aspects. Thus 'annual contracts' have been replaced by longer-term 'service agreements'. Fundholding GP practices have given way to larger and more bureaucratic primary care groups.

It is far from clear that this has resulted in significant cost savings or any savings at all. Had there been savings of the order of £100 million it would, of necessity, have been reflected in the laying off of thousands of managerial staff. There have been no reports of this, nor of managers being retrained to switch to 'frontline care'.

It is indisputably desirable to minimise administrative costs in the NHS so as to maximise the share of the taxpayers' money going into front line healthcare. The administrative costs of ECRs were in line with the NHS average; we have yet to see how much the OATs will cost to administer. I am certainly not advocating a return to the ECR system. Reportedly one of its most complex and costly features was its requirement that purchasers pay the actual costs incurred by each hospital for each type of operation. The new system requires PCGs to pay hospitals that treat their patients a standard amount (set at the national average cost for each type of operation). That is simpler and should be retained.

Given that a system exists for transferring money from primary care groups to the trusts that treat their patients, it is far from clear that the additional costs of allowing patients greater choice of which hospital to use would be significant.

Of course choice and diversity of provision in any service always appear to involve 'unnecessary costs'. State monopolies were thought to have a clear headstart in efficiency by eliminating 'wasteful' choice and diversity. But the clear and unequivocal evidence in sector after sector is that the anticipated savings from eliminating choice and diversity are invariably dwarfed by the higher costs resulting from loss of pressure to improve efficiency and relate resources to users' needs.

Standardisation can produce cost savings – as Henry Ford proclaimed when he said 'you can have any colour so long as it's black'. But there is a trade-off between realising those savings and catering for users' diverse preferences. Where users have choice, it is they who ultimately determine the balance between standardisation and variety. Very rarely are the savings from providing a totally standardised service or product sufficient to outweigh the loss of all variety. If that is so with commercial products surely we should be even more wary about trying to standardise provision of something as intrinsically personal as health.

Choice resulted in 'hospital competing against hospital'

The prime minister has repeatedly claimed that the internal market meant that 'hospital competed against hospital'.[19] The implication that competition is intrinsically destructive reveals how skin deep is the prime minister's conversion to liberal economics. However, for the very different reasons I explained in my Butler Memorial Lecture,[20] healthcare is different from any normal service. As a result, it is *not* suitable for provision via a competitive free market model. It is and should be largely financed by the taxpayer and provided by the NHS. Those who dress up sensible reforms of the NHS in the language of economic analysis, managerial jargon or pseudo-business terminology discredit these changes.

Greater patient choice within the NHS will not result in pitting hospitals against each other. At best it will encourage NHS hospitals to strive to excel in caring for patients.

Choice meant that in the ECR system 'patients could find themselves the subject of heated debate between GPs, NHS trusts and health authorities over who would pay for treatment'[21]

To the extent that this was true, it was unacceptable and needed to be resolved. Such problems could only arise because of lack of clarity about where responsibility for funding lay. It is not a necessary consequence of patient choice. If anything, it was a symptom of reluctance of the NHS bureaucracy to accommodate even the small amount of patient choice that remained under the system introduced in 1990.

If patient choice were the norm rather than the exception the responsibility of the purchaser to fund each patient's care would be clearly established. Such problems would then disappear. It is significant that no analogous problems are reported in the school system where funds *automatically* follow the pupil.

'Choice is irrelevant: the NHS simply needs more money'

The implication of this argument is that there is a specific amount of money and resources that would satisfy demand for healthcare. In fact, the amount that could be spent on health is almost limitless. What is essential is to get the maximum value for patients out of whatever resources Parliament makes available to the NHS.

Money is likely to be put to the best use if it is allocated in accordance with patients' wishes, if it rewards excellence and if it encourages sub-standard hospitals to improve their care and efficiency. Only a system in which patients and their GPs can choose their care and in which money follows that choice will achieve that.

'Choice is the prelude to privatising the NHS'

My departure from the front bench followed a high-octane row about my affirmation that there are distinct limits to the scope for private provision in healthcare. So I trust no one suspects me of now plotting wholesale privatisation by other means.

I want to see more choice within the NHS which should remain funded by the taxpayer. Allowing NHS patients to choose between different NHS hospitals, with the cost of their care still funded by the taxpayer, does not constitute privatisation.

At present, the NHS does purchase some healthcare from non-NHS hospitals to the tune of £450 million. It would not be possible to extend patients' right to choose to include non-NHS hospitals since private hospitals will often charge more than the standard NHS cost of providing that treatment. However, if patients and GPs can find hospitals outside the NHS that provide treatment at below the standard cost of that treatment, clearly they should be permitted to use them. It would release taxpayers' money and reduce pressures on the NHS.

It would also be possible to expand patient choice further on the lines of the imaginative recent proposal by Ruth Lea.[22] Under this proposal, patients could be referred to a private hospital even if it cost more than the NHS so long as the patient paid the excess above the standard NHS charge for that treatment that would be met by the taxpayer.

5. Information and patient choice

The one prevalent objection to patient choice not mentioned in the previous chapter is that patients – even with the help of their GPs – may lack the knowledge necessary to make informed choices.

Clearly they will need access to information about waiting times, specialisms, mortality and success rates at each hospital. We need to develop a system in which patients can find this sort of information at their GP's surgery or even over the internet. Much of the information they need is already collected even if it is not currently made available to patients.

Waiting times

Patients and GPs will want to know the likely time they will have to wait for a consultation and subsequent treatment at alternative hospitals. The NHS publishes data on out-patient waiting times by speciality for each NHS trust each quarter.[23]

Unfortunately, this only shows the proportion of patients seen within thirteen weeks of written referral by a GP (25 per cent have to wait more than thirteen weeks). This information is not a great deal of use. Moreover, it relates to the trust rather than the individual consultant and is about waiting times in the recent past rather than the current wait for a new appointment.

Ideally the patient needs to know the actual waiting time for each consultant. The National Waiting List Helpline gathers and holds information about the length of wait for a first out-patient appointment for virtually every consultant surgeon in the country. Sadly, the Department of Health grant for this helpline was ended and it is now maintained with a grant from a charitable family trust and support from Nuffield Hospitals.

Moreover, hospital consultants apparently give this information to the helpline somewhat reluctantly and only on the understanding that it will be made available to GPs in confidence and is not for wider publication. As a result few patients and not all GPs are aware that it is available at all.

However, helpline organisers say they have 'helped many thousands get treated in a timely fashion if they were willing to travel – we probably helped save some lives. Thousands of others have been saved years of unnecessary pain.'[24]

Specialisation

The more frequently a surgeon performs a treatment the better he is likely to become at doing it. He will also become more familiar with the complications that only arise infrequently.[25] Other things being equal, most of us would prefer to be operated on by a specialist surgeon rather than an inexperienced generalist. There is no publicly available source of information on the extent of specialisation of different hospitals. However, the government does have a database of hospital episode statistics recording how many operations each hospital in England carries out in each category.

Hospital trusts are not compelled to report to this database on the frequency of individual procedures performed. Nevertheless, some do provide this type of information so presumably it could be collected comprehensively.

The National Institute for Clinical Excellence provides information that patients can use about a particular procedure or treatment so that better-informed patients will ask better questions of their health practitioners.

Mortality/success rates

The information many patients would like most of all is the most controversial – data on the mortality and success rates of performing specific treatments at each hospital. The usefulness of such data is disputed. However, raw figures can be misleading. A hospital that treats particularly severe cases will have a worse death rate than one dealing with much milder cases of the same illness. *In extremis*, a hospice for terminally ill cancer patients may give the most wonderful care to the dying, but will have a far higher mortality figure than a hospital treating early stage cancers.

Nonetheless, more data about hospital performance is being collected and issued. Also methods of adjusting output data for the seriousness of patients' pre-operative conditions have been developed.

So patients need guidance on how to make use of such information. Certainly if parents had had access to the mortality figures of infant heart surgery at the Bristol unit (and if they had had any choice) many would have moved to a different hospital. That would have provoked remedial action at Bristol far sooner than actually took place. Fewer parents would have faced the tragedy of losing their child.

Until recently, official figures for hospital discharges lumped together people who were cured and those who left in coffins. The last government took the bold step of publishing some hospital mortality statistics in Scotland. The medical profession was involved in that decision – taking the wise view that once it had been decided to compile the data for internal use, it was better to publish it rather than let it leak out. The public reaction was more mature than many feared.

The English NHS has followed suit.[26] Most of the indicators now published are fairly general – for example 'deaths in hospital within 30 days of surgery for emergency admissions'. Similar figures for non-emergency admissions are shown as a separate indicator. The figures are age standardised and show a 95 per cent confidence interval for each NHS trust. Another invaluable indicator is 'the rate of emergency re-admission to hospital within 28 days of discharge from hospital'. This is used as a proxy indicator for avoidable re-admissions. These can vary between hospitals from fewer than 20 per cent to over 70 per cent.

One of the few indicators relating to a specific condition is the rate of 'deaths in hospital within 30 days of emergency admission with a heart attack (myocardial infarction) for patients aged 50 and over'. It shows that the risk of death is at least twice as high in some trusts as in others. Higher rates might be expected in, for example, teaching hospitals taking patients needing specialist intervention but these variations occur between general hospitals.

The most valuable information would be mortality and success rates not just for every hospital but for each individual surgeon. The medical profession in Britain is still resistant to publishing information in such telling detail.[27] Nonetheless, experience of countries where this has been done is very encouraging.

In the early 1990s, the New York State Department of Health decided to study the relationship between the frequency with which surgeons performed a surgical procedure and the mortality rate.[28] The procedure studied was coronary artery bypass graft surgery. The results showed clearly that surgeons who carry out a procedure frequently tend to achieve significantly lower mortality rates. This was true even when the figures were adjusted for different mixes of patients with different pre-operative risk factors.

The department was the first in the United States to publish mortality rates for each of its hospitals. Initially, the data relating to individual surgeons was kept confidential. However, as a result of a court ruling under freedom of information laws, the state was obliged to publish that data as well. Over the four years covered by the study, the mortality rate for this operation declined significantly.

The mortality for low volume surgeons (performing 50 or fewer operations a year) fell by 60 per cent. The highest volume surgeons (over 150 operations a year) saw mortality rates fall by 34 per cent. And the percentage of patients being treated by low-volume surgeons fell by a quarter.

The improvement was not primarily because patients all chose to go to the surgeons with low mortality rates. Rather, once the data was public, hospitals pre-empted that decision by 'restricting the surgical privileges of some low-volume surgeons'. Other low-volume surgeons retired or gave up performing this particular operation.

The combination of information, publication and choice proved to be a powerful weapon for improving quality.

The patient's advocate

Historically, the GP has been the primary source of information and advice to patients. I have tacitly assumed that this will continue to be the case if proper choice is restored.

However, it has been questioned whether that places too much reliance on GPs. Are they geared to act as the patients' advocates, seeking the best deal for patients rather than the most convenient option? There is a risk that GPs have been so much under the thumb of the NHS bureaucracy that some may identify with its interests.

Others may have limited knowledge of the options available. So they would simply refer their patients to consultants they meet locally or knew at medical school. An advocacy role will require a more pro-active approach on behalf of their patients.

Re-establishing the right to choice and giving it financial muscle will itself set in train forces that will stimulate a more patient-oriented approach by GPs.

But that will take time. Fortunately, that process is likely to be accelerated as patients increasingly make use of alternative options for self-diagnosis and self-referral. This is being given a boost by NHS Direct and NHS Online. Both encourage patients to take an informed view of their own health needs. Even before these came on stream more patients were, in effect, referring themselves by going direct to accident and emergency units rather than visiting their GPs.

NHS Online apart, the government's approach to information and quality is increasingly centralised – it is based on the command and control model. The newly-established National Institute of Clinical Excellence will garner available information and decide which treatments are most (cost) effective. Its view will then be imposed through the NHS.

A new Commission for Health Improvement will then try to impose standards from the centre. National Service Frameworks will be agreed for each major care area and disease group to ensure 'greater consistency in the availability and quality of services right across the NHS'.[29]

Of course, central initiatives are necessary to improve standards. But they are not sufficient and, to the extent that they impose uniformity, they may hinder improvement. They need to be reinforced by harnessing patient power to generate bottom-up pressures for improvement.

Modern technology would make a different approach possible. Information could be made universally available and accessible. In the longer run, it would be possible to establish a web site for each major diagnostic group. It would contain information or treatment options, medical evidence of their effectiveness and facts about each hospital's performance.

More assertive and better-informed patients – with or without their GP's consent – are also likely to seek more than one consultant's opinion. Ministers recently confirmed that patients do still have the right to a second opinion.[30] Presumably the reason it is rarely exercised is partly that few patients realise that they have that right. In addition, given lengthy waiting times, few patients want a further delay to obtain another consultation.

Clearly, there would be adverse cost implications if patients routinely sought advice from several consultants. This apparently used to be very much the culture in France. It has recently had to be curtailed amidst great controversy. Britain has the opposite culture and there would be some benefit if consultants knew that their advice might be compared with that of another consultant.

6. Specialisation and choice

The presumption underlying Labour's new arrangements is that patients should go to their local hospital for all common treatments. However, they recognise that GPs will wish to refer patients with complex or rare conditions to specialist centres.

Under the previous system fundholders could enter into contracts with specialist centres. They would usually draw up the contract on the basis of the number of patients needing such specialised treatment in previous years. If the fundholders had not previously had any patients with that condition or the treatment was new, they could use the ECR system to finance their patients' treatment.

In the new system, primary care groups enter into service agreements covering all conditions. Development of new services is the responsibility of the region, which is expected to commission specialised services. These changes are causing serious problems partly because such agreements simply are not in place. GPs are not allowed to use the OAT arrangements as a substitute for ECRs.

A leading neurosurgeon, Tipu Aziz of the Radcliffe Infirmary in Oxford, has warned that the reforms are starving specialist centres of resources.In an open letter to Tony Blair he stated, 'Now with the chaos of the OATs system I am told that monies follow approved treatment after two years – so the hospital runs a deficit for that period. Also, if local providers offer an equivalent service, irrespective of their experience and results, patients cannot be referred to an experienced centre. (So why blame the Bristol surgeons, as the present system will ensure that many more such scenarios will repeat themselves?)'[31]

Neurologist Professor Findley, who founded the National Tremor Foundation argued that 'the previous referral system worked very well, unlike OATs ... Centres of excellence that thrived under the previous referral system are being strangled and yet the problem is hardly being discussed'.[32] Problems seem to be particularly great where new treatments are being developed and where the specialist treatment is not within one of the priority areas defined by the government.

A coalition of charities including the Parkinson's Disease Society, Scope, ASBAH and the Neurological Alliance have also highlighted problems affecting their specialisms. They say:

> 'Patients are not receiving the specialist treatment which it has been recommended they receive.'
>
> 'Many specialist centres including Oxford Radcliffe Infirmary, Charing Cross Hospital and centres in Edinburgh and Liverpool have stopped treating NHS patients.'
>
> 'The net effect is that patients, who would have received the specialist neurology treatment that they need under the ECR system just one year ago, are not able to get the funding required under the OATs system.'

They are not advocating a return to the ECR system as such. As a short-term solution, they suggest that the Department of Health give a written undertaking to specialist centres that they can go ahead and treat out-of-area patients on their waiting lists and that funding will follow.

In the longer-term, they want to incorporate specialist services into a framework of 'disease management'. This would involve considering all the costs involved in a chronic patient's support – residential care, pharmaceutical costs, nursing costs, surgery and social security benefits. West Surrey Health Authority has adopted this approach to patients with Parkinson's disease and saved over £73,000 on the social services budget alone. This was achieved by better attuned treatment and access to support reducing or removing some patients' needs for more expensive residential or nursing care.

A system in which patients were referred by their GP to the specialist centre of their choice, with money following them, would overcome existing problems, encourage development of new treatments and be compatible with the sort of cross-budget disease management recommended by the Neurological Alliance.

Choice is a potent weapon in improving quality and efficiency. Where users of a service – be it public or private – have a choice between alternative suppliers, those suppliers know that if they do not match the best in quality and efficiency they will lose users and therefore revenues. So they have to improve. Best practice then spreads throughout the service.

But where users of a service have little choice best practice does not spread. That is one of the problems in the NHS. According to some studies, Britain has one of the lowest survival rates for bowel cancer of any country in Europe. Yet at the same time, the bowel cancer unit with the highest survival rates in the world is in Britain – at the North Hampshire Hospital. Their approach, based on precision surgery, not only saves lives but is also cheaper in so far as there are fewer colostomies and less chemotherapy. It has been copied in Sweden, Holland and Slovenia. But there seems to be little incentive for it to spread within the NHS. If patients from other health authorities were allowed to choose to go to North Hampshire, surely other NHS hospitals would copy its approach rather than lose patients and resources.

Absence of specialisation in more common treatments

Other things being equal, most people would prefer to be treated at their local hospital. When we are sick most of us would prefer not to have to travel too far. And we want to be near friends and relatives to visit us and take us home.

Nonetheless, we would not want to have a lung transplant in our local cottage hospital however convenient. Few people think twice about travelling a considerable distance to have a major operation performed in a specially equipped hospital by a distinguished surgeon. We take it for granted that the sickest may need to travel furthest. Yet, paradoxically, we assume that people with lesser conditions should not even be allowed to travel to a specialist centre.

At present, the NHS only finances specialist centres to treat rare conditions or to perform highly specialised operations. Yet there is a strong case for also developing centres that specialise in common operations. There is great scope for increasing efficiency in this way just as a measure of specialisation drives down costs and improves quality in every other area of life.

Other countries have specialist centres for common operations like cataracts. Such centres can operate seven days a week and 24 hours a day to make maximum use of theatre capacity. Moreover, patients can book in at a time to suit their convenience. Surgeons specialising in a specific area become extremely skilled and familiar with the less frequent complications that may arise. So quality is enhanced and costs are reduced.

Such centres would develop naturally if patients could positively chose to be treated at specialist centres even though they were further away than their local hospital. Because patients would be free to use specialist centres or not they would not arouse antagonism. By contrast, if the NHS set up such centres under its normal bureaucratic planning procedures, there would be enormous controversy and allegations that patients were being dragooned into using them to cut costs.

Ministers have responded to this suggestion by raising the spectre of a few specialist centres entirely replacing local hospitals. This is nonsense. Where comparatively minor operations are concerned, some people will be attracted to a regional centre offering immediate, more convenient and high-quality treatment – but many will still prefer to go to their local hospital. In most other spheres, a few large specialist centres co-exist with smaller local units.

If money following patient choice does lead to units specialising in hernias, cataracts and so on, they are likely to be at the forefront of developing new, more effective and more efficient methods of treatment. These will spread to general hospitals that would never have had the resources individually to develop new procedures themselves.

7. Quality and choice

A central aim of introducing more patient choice is to drive up the quality of all aspects of care within the NHS, not just clinical success rates.

The horrifying catalogue of neglect, slipshod nursing and sheer incompetence reported in VT Walker's diary account of one family's experience in the NHS is not typical.[33] But it illustrates how bad things can get in a system where people have no choice.

I am struck by the number of people who have mentioned to me that specific hospitals are visibly dirty. In some hospitals spilt food or even urine can be left for hours before it is cleaned up, whereas other hospitals are kept spotlessly clean at all times. People who have visited hospitals with poor standards of cleanliness often comment, 'I would never choose to go there as a patient'. They do not realise that if it has been selected by their PCG they will effectively have no choice.

The problem of illness resulting from infections picked up in hospital has recently been highlighted. No fewer than 9 per cent of NHS beds at any one time are occupied by patients who are there because of infections caught since their arrival.[34]

This is an appallingly high overall level and it must be much higher in the worst hospitals. Ideally, the incidence of such problems should be published. But even if that information is not made available patients and, even more, their GPs do get to know.

As Harriet Harman said in 1990 (when criticising the Conservative reforms):

> 'When GPs decide to refer patients for treatment, they have the advantage of having seen patients come back from hos-

> pitals after operations and other treatment. They develop opinions on where patients have been happiest to go and on where there have been fewest post-operative complications. In the absence of any other data about quality, the GP's instinct about where to refer patients is the most important available indicator of quality.'

She was right to argue then that GPs should be free to use that experience in referring patients. Quality of care is not just about *objective* aspects like clinical outcomes, cleanliness and risk of infection. It is also about responding to patients' *subjective* preferences.

As the NHS offers more choice, it must provide more diversity – different styles of caring tailored to patients' preferences. Many patients prefer to be treated in single sex wards but do not at present have that option in the hospital selected by their PCG. Other patients would prefer to be treated by a doctor or consultant of their own sex. Patients have different preferences as far as the whole ethos of a hospital is concerned. Some would like to be involved much more in decisions about the method of treatment whereas others prefer to leave that to the consultant. Increasingly, people want to know about alternative therapies. Even if these are not available on the NHS information about them could be more readily available.

Moreover, the quality of care is a function of everything the hospital does that affects the patient, from arranging appointments, through initial reception and visiting arrangements, to discharge and aftercare. Historically, the NHS has been notorious for the coldness and incompetence of these aspects of care. The effect of making money follow patients' choice should encourage hospitals to customise their care.

8. Efficiency and choice

There are wide differences in the costs incurred by different hospitals for identical operations. For example, the average cost for an elective opthamological procedure – cataract removal with a lens implant –was £699 in 1998. Yet costs in NHS hospitals range from £337 to £1,659. Similarly, the cost of a primary hip replacement averaged £3,678 but individual hospital costs range from £1,834 to £6,494.

Information on the cost of a range of different treatments is published for every hospital. Yet even if you want to save the taxpayer money and be treated in a more cost-effective hospital than that selected by your PCG, you can no longer do so.

In practice, that is unlikely to be the main criterion on which most of us would choose where to be treated. Nonetheless, a maxim of leading businesses is that 'quality costs less'. Time and again experience shows that improvements that raise quality also cut costs and vice versa. It would be surprising if that were not also often true in medicine. In business, the classic example is the focus on 'getting it right first time', cutting out the costs of repairs and making good. Likewise, better quality healthcare would mean fewer avoidable readmissions (which can vary two or threefold between hospitals). We should surely care far more about getting it right first time when treating people than when assembling machinery.

Where improved quality and efficiency go hand in hand there are few problems. But patients want to be reassured that the quality of their care will not be sacrificed to save money. The emphasis of the 1990 internal market reforms was to give purchasers an incentive to select the lower cost provider, other things being equal. Purchasers were billed by hospitals an amount reflecting the actual cost of the operation in that unit. Under that system, it was quite easy to stir up fears that quality would be sacrificed to save costs.

Under the new arrangements, providers bill PCGs at a standard price reflecting the national average cost of each type of operation – *not* the cost in that particular hospital. So purchasers face the same price whichever hospital they enter into a service agreement with. I propose that we stick with that system. It is simpler and less bureaucratic. There is no question of patients having to go to the cheapest hospital.

Hospitals with above-average costs have an incentive to bring them down to the average – otherwise they will overrun their budgets, or have to ration by longer waiting times (as at present), or do both. The hospitals that perform a treatment more efficiently than average would make a surplus by treating out-of-area patients. So they would be able to expand. Of course, the most cost-effective hospitals will not be able to attract more patients by charging less since the patient's purchaser would pay a standard tariff for all hospitals. So hospitals will only be able to expand if they are *both* more efficient and offer a higher quality of treatment that attracts more referrals.

9. Feasibility of choice

Could the hospital service cope if GPs were genuinely free to refer patients to the hospital of their choice? Whenever it is proposed to introduce user choice into a centrally planned system the existing bureaucracy reacts with horror. I remember being told in almost hysterical terms by the Chairman of the Central Electricity Generating Board that it was 'mad' even to suggest that the centrally planned electricity system could be replaced by a market in electricity. There were (unspecified) technical obstacles. Only a layman could suggest such an impractical idea. It would lead to chaos.

Events proved him wrong. Such a market now exists. There were no insurmountable technical obstacles. It was introduced smoothly. There was no chaos. Instead it resulted in the doubling of productivity within four years.

He was a very clever man. He knew infinitely more about the existing electricity industry than I did. But he could not move from the familiar paradigm of a centrally administered system to envisage the unfamiliar notion of multiple decision-makers interacting and adjusting to each other.

Undoubtedly, some NHS managers will react in a similar way. They will find alarming in the extreme the idea of allowing tens of thousands of GPs to refer millions of patients to the hospitals of their choice instead of those chosen in advance by the health service bureaucracy. There will be (unspecified) technical obstacles. Only a layman could suggest it. It will lead to chaos.

Many managers argue that they must know in advance where patients will go. How else can they plan adequate provision? Planning requires certainty. So they must have means of channelling patients to the hospitals they have provided. If not, some will be empty and others will have huge waiting lists.

Such a reaction is as understandable as it is predictable. But further analysis – as well as practical experience – should dispel such fears. Managers already cope with uncertainty. They have no say over which individuals will be ill, where, when and with what illnesses. They make predictions that rely on the law of large numbers to smooth things out. Unless there are epidemics or disasters a fairly stable pattern of demand for treatment emerges in each area. It may evolve over time but it gives a basis on which managers can plan the pattern of health facilities.

Likewise if thousands of doctors and millions of patients make individual decisions about referrals the law of large numbers will operate. A fairly stable pattern will emerge. It, too, may evolve but it will give a basis for planning the location of health facilities.

If the pattern of illness in an area turns out differently from what managers predicted and planned for, there is no self-adjusting mechanism to match supply and demand for healthcare. Managers have to do their best to re-allocate resources to cope.

By contrast, if patient choices result in a pattern of referrals different from what managers predicted and planned for there is a self-righting process. Patients will adapt their choice of hospital to (among other things) the availability of treatment and length of waiting times.

As the Director of the College of Health said, 'It doesn't make sense to impose limits on referring patients from overstretched hospitals to those with spare capacity.'[35]

Normally, the overall effect of patients' choices should actually reduce the pressure on the most over-loaded hospitals. Some patients will opt to go to hospitals outside their area that have spare capacity and shorter waiting times. This will ease the burden on those with longer waiting lists. Other patients may choose to be referred to hospitals with a lower level of avoidable re-admission than their local hospital. That will reduce the need for unnecessary treatments. Others may choose hospitals with lower rates of in-hospital infection, which will also reduce exposure to the risk of unnecessary stays in hospital.

Patients will only choose to be referred to hospitals with longer waiting times than their local hospital if they and their GP believe that the improvement in quality of care makes the delay worthwhile. Any resultant increase in waiting times for non-urgent elective operations in popular hospitals both indicates that they should expand and provides the resources for them to do so.

If so many patients opt to be referred out of area that the local hospital is left underutilised that is *not* a reason for dragooning patients back into that hospital. It is a reason for inquiring why it is failing to attract sufficient patients – and then remedying any defects. Central planning conceals problems. Delegated choice will reveal previously hidden problems. When money follows choice it will jump start the process of improving failing hospitals. Hospitals may need the power to change senior personnel to regain public confidence and convince patients that higher standards of clinical performance are being introduced.

In practice, freedom of choice for patients and their GPs will not lead to any massive movements away from local hospitals. The numbers exercising the choice to use an out-of-area hospital are likely to be fairly modest. But it is always changes at the margin that are crucially important. Marginal losses of users can trigger major improvements in any service. And over time, cumulative movements of patients followed by resources can feed the growth of centres of excellence specialising in particular treatments.

Although planners raise the spectre of patients moving en masse away from less good hospitals, precipitating their collapse, in practice that rarely happens since movements are incremental. Yet, paradoxically, mass withdrawal of patients is the only threat an NHS purchaser can wield in negotiating with a failing hospital. The primary care group can scarcely threaten to send 10 per cent of its patients elsewhere next year unless the trust improves, for example, its cleanliness. What would the PCG say to the remaining 90 per cent whom it continued to send to a hospital it deemed inferior? How would the PCG select the 10 per cent of patients to be sent to a better but possibly more distant hospital? The only equitable way would be to give their patients the option – which is precisely what I propose.

Similar concerns were expressed about schools when the reforms making money follow the pupil were introduced. In particular, it was feared that if less popular schools lost resources when they lost pupils, they would be plunged into a spiral of decline. Experience has shown that more often than not loss of resources was the one thing capable of prompting an inadequate school to make real improvements. Moreover, movements in pupil numbers between unpopular and successful schools were rarely as dramatic as people had imagined (partly because popular schools could not expand overnight). So there was usually time for schools to demonstrate improvement.

There is nonetheless a serious problem resulting from parental choice in education but it is unlikely to be relevant to hospitals. That is the problem of social segregation.

Other things being equal, schools in higher income zones in any district are more likely to have a higher proportion of able, academic and motivated pupils and few problem children than schools in more deprived areas. Parents know that children learn from each other as well as from teachers. So parents living in deprived areas who do not mind their children travelling further to school are likely to want to send them to schools in the more prosperous areas. If those schools are able to expand, the schools in the most deprived areas will shrink or close entirely. If schools places are allocated on the basis of zoning, then parents' ability to exercise choice becomes a function of house prices.

These are serious issues arising from choice in education. However, similar problems are *not* likely to affect choice of hospitals. Patients do not select hospitals on the basis of the social class of fellow patients. In any case hospitals serve larger areas than schools, invariably covering a wide social mix. Scarcely anyone buys a house to live in the catchment area of a particular hospital.

Of course, mechanisms would need to exist to cope with hospitals that fail to remedy their deficiencies and continue to lose patients and resources. The only options in such circumstances are central intervention; takeover by or merger with a more successfully managed hospital; or closure. Those are the ultimate sanctions within the present system. Under patient choice they would be invoked more rarely as choice provoked improvements.

Such extreme remedies are bound to be traumatic. That is especially the case under the present system where any decision to close or merge a hospital provokes a political backlash. It is seen as the arbitrary act of a distant bureaucracy ignoring local wishes. Local people are not given any information about the relative performance of their hospital prior to its closure. They have been encouraged to believe it is as good as any other. So closure seems all the more arbitrary. Experience of such uproars has probably discouraged the NHS from some desirable closures and mergers.

If the prospect of closure or merger came about under a system where patients and GPs made informed choices, it would still be painful. But it would be mitigated by the fact that local people would be seen to have been voting with their feet. It will be harder for protesters to pretend that their local hospital is everyone's favourite institution. As a result, the NHS would find it a little easier to make changes. No system should be ossified with a given pattern of resources while population shifts, new structures are needed and preferences change. But it is both better and politically easier to make changes in response to patient choice rather than by bureaucratic diktat.

Rationing and choice

Another practical concern is the compatibility of a system where money follows patient choice with the need to ration care within a given budget.

At least until recently, politicians of all colours were reluctant to use the word 'rationing'. But every health system needs some device to restrict demand within available supply. Rationing is the device that dare not speak its name.

Market economists sometimes talk as if rationing exists only in state-financed health system because 'they provide care largely free at the point of demand' (or as non-economists would say, when people are ill). In fact, private insurance schemes equally 'provide care largely free at the point of demand'. So they too have to restrict expenditure to match aggregate insurance premiums – by restricting conditions covered and treatments used. Otherwise their premiums would have to go up.

The NHS has been particularly effective at rationing. It does so by a mixture of decisions about priorities implemented by GPs and consultants and by queueing and delays. What has made this so effective is a mixture of opacity and deference. Neither patients nor their relatives could see clearly when possible treatments were being withheld and they were too deferential to question medical judgement.

Consumerist attitudes are beginning to change that. As a result, decisions about priorities are becoming more transparent. That process is inevitably going to go further. Patient choice is bound to speed up the move from rationing which is implicit and unquestioned to that which is objective and transparent.

That will be a painful process to manage though in the long run it must be to the good. However, It does mean that introducing a system of patient choice will accelerate the need to develop a new process for determining priorities. The experience of other countries who have trod this route ahead of us will be beneficial, notably Oregon and New Zealand.[36]

Liam Fox's promise to give a guarantee of treatment within maximum waiting times related to the severity of a patient's medical condition as determined by clinicians not politicians is very sensible. Indeed, it will become essential as the pressures for transparency increase.

10. Proposals for choice

How can patients exercise genuine, informed and effective choice within the NHS? The three key steps are:

- Restore the right of GPs to refer patients to the hospital of their choice in practice as well as theory.
- Publish information by hospital and specialty on waiting times, frequency of performing each treatment, success/mortality rates (adjusted by severity of illness) and so on. And make that information available in doctors' surgeries and on the internet.
- Make sure that the taxpayers' money follows the patient simply and speedily.

The last step is the least visible to the public but the most crucial. It ensures that choice does not just allow patients to swell the waiting lists of the hospital of their choice.

It is also the only way to remove the administrative obstacles that at present prevent GPs and patients from exercising their theoretical right of referral to the hospital of their choice.

It is important that the process of money following patient be as streamlined as possible. So the amount for each treatment should be the current 'referrence cost'. There is no question of returning to charges based on the actual cost level of each hospital. Nor is there any need to re-introduce a process of prior authorisation of each referral. This was said to be the source of much time-consuming haggling under the ECR regime.

Health authorities do not double guess decisions by GPs to refer a patient to a local hospital. There is no reason for them to double guess GPs when they refer a patient to a hospital in another area.

Last, but not least, the transfer of money to the hospital treating a patient must be speedy and direct. There is no reason for it to be delayed into the next accounting year, let alone take two years as it can at present. The key to speed is *automaticity*, which should be easily achieved once the process of prior authorisation of referrals is abolished.

Notes

1. Most transnational studies show that beyond a certain point extra spending on health produces little or no improvement in life expectancy or other measures of health outcomes.

One much quoted study seems to show that the percentage of people surviving more than 5 years after cancer treatment is lower in the UK than continental countries. The source document (Eurocare-2), however, explicitly warns that the figures may not be comparable for a range of reasons.

2. Lord Lever once said that half the money spent on advertising was wasted. The trouble was he didn't know which half. I suspect the same is true of expenditure on healthcare. But until we know which part of health spending is unnecessary we are faced with a huge and growing cost.

3. *New Statesman*, 24 April 2000.

4. The relevance of problems experienced with choice in education to an analogous system in health is discussed in chapter 9.

5. Bacon AD, *Doctors, Patients and the NHS*, published by SSP Books, London NW1 7DS.

6. Patients may be referred on to tertiary specialist centres by a consultant.

7. Webster C, *The Health Services Since the War*, vol II, HMSO, London, p609.

8. *Working for Patients*, White Paper, Department of Health, London, January 1989.

9. Letter from John Denham to author, August 1999.

10. *Hansard*, 12 April 2000.

11. *Hansard*, 21 December 1999, col 663.

12. *Hansard*, 1 February 2000, col 201.

13. Health Service Circular No 1999/117.

14. *Health Service Journal*, February 1999.

15. John Denham, in *Hansard*, 21 December 1999, col 663.

16. Parliamentary Question, 25 November 1999.

17. John Denham, in *Hansard*, 21 December 1999, col 663.

18. *New Statesman*, 17 January 2000.

19. Tony Blair, in *Hansard*, 31 March 1999, col 1086.

20. The Butler Memorial Lecture, 20 April 1999. Transcript obtainable from Peter Lilley, The House of Commons, London SW1A 0AA.

21. Letter from Denham to author,

15 October 1999.

22. Lea R, 2000, *Health Care in the UK: The need for reform*, Institute of Directors, London.

23. *Hansard*, 29 February 2000.

24. Maxine Rigg, quoted in *Health Service Journal*, February 1999.

25. *The Relationship Between Hospital Volumes and Quality of Health Outcomes*, University of York, CRD Report 8, part 1.

26. *Hansard*, 15 March 2000, col 236-7W.

27. There are legitimate concerns that a surgeon may be reluctant to operate on high-risk patients for fear of depressing their success rate. This reinforces the need for weighting by pre-operative condition, which has been done successfully in the United States.

28. Hanna E L et al, 1995, 'The Decline in Coronary Artery By-pass Graft Surgery Mortality in New York State', *Journal of American Medical Association*, 18 January.

29. 'The New NHS', House of Commons Command Paper 3807, December 1997.

30. *Hansard*, 13 March 2000.

31. Open letter to Tony Blair, *Daily Telegraph*, 17 January 2000.

32. Letters page, *Daily Telegraph*, 17 January 2000.

33. Walker VT, *In Whose Hands*, published by Lantern 1999, 1 High Street, Barmouth, Wales LL42 1DS.

34. National Audit Office, 2000, *The Management and Control of Hospital Acquired Infection in Acute NHS Trust in England*, HMSO, London.

35. *Health Service Journal*, February 1999.

36. Coulter A and Ham C, eds, 2000, *The Global Challenge of Healthcare Rationing*', Open University Press.